Dedication

I would like to dedicate this book to the people who always encouraged me to look past my imperfections and manifest the talents Yah blessed me with. My mother, who has always been my number 1 fan and my biggest cheerleader. My Pop Pop,who told me the sky is the limit. My husband, who never lets me sell myself short. And my wonderful sister in the faith, Ahava, who watered, pruned, and nurtured the writer in me. She ignited the flame, which manifested itself into the book you are reading today.

The Three Little Hebrew Boys & The Big Bad Wolf

Written by Keturah Rena
Illustrated by Tajha Alston

Once upon a time, there was a big bad wolf named Nebuchadnezzar, king of Babylon. Everyone called him Nebby for short. Now, King Nebby was notoriously rich. He owned lots of cows and lambs, houses and lands. The Wolf King always hosted the most elaborate feasts. All Nebby's friends from around the kingdom came to attend, and they were in awe of his extravagant engagements.

Nebby's kingdom was so big he couldn't tend to everything himself. So, he had lots of boys and girls who worked for him and helped him with the ins and outs of his daily operations. Living under the rule of his kingdom, were a particular group of boys who were blessed from on high by Elohim. The three boys were Hebrew Yisraelites of the tribe of Yahudah from Yerusalem. Their Hebrew names were: Hananiah (Yah is gracious), Mishael (who is what El is), and Azariah (Yah has helped). But everyone called them by the names King Nebby gave them: Shadrach, Meshach, and Abednego.

Shadrach, Meshach, and Abednego held really important jobs. King Nebby assigned them to oversee all the affairs of the province in Babylon. Life for these three little Hebrew boys was going smoothly. They had good paying jobs, nice houses, and some of the finest clothes in the kingdom. This made some other boys envious. So, they came up with a plan to stir up King Nebby's anger against the Hebrew boys.

The envious boys in Babylon found their opportunity to turn King Nebby against the three little Hebrew boys when the king threw an elaborate feast to reveal his new statue. The king's statue was carved out of gold. It stood 90 feet tall (three-score cubits) and 9 feet wide (six cubits). If you want to know how big that is, you can think of the statue being 9 royal elephants tall and 1 elephant wide.

At the revealing of his statue, King Nebby made an unusual request:

"Hear ye! Hear ye!" cried the Herald. "To you it is commanded, O people, nations, and languages, that at what time ye hear the sound of the cornet, flute, harp, sackbut, psaltery, dulcimer, and all kinds of musick, ye fall down and worship the golden image that Nebuchadnezzar the king hath set up: and whoso falleth not down and worshippeth shall the same hour be cast into the midst of a burning fiery furnace. " (Daniel 3:4-5)

Do you remember the mean, bratty boys I told you about earlier? The ones who didn't like like our friends? They're called Chaldeans. They knew the Children of Yisrael were a set apart people. They didn't drink the offered wine, nor eat the abominable food. They didn't worship the same way, or the same gods. The Children of Yisrael only worshiped Yahuah, the Supreme Elohim. The Chaldeans used this against the three little Hebrew boys: Shadrach, Meshach, and Abednego. They knew there was NO way our three little Hebrew friends were going to bow down to King Nebby's statue.

When the king found out the Yahudim were disobeying his proclamation, he became filled with rage. King Nebby got so mad he wanted to go question the three little Hebrew boys himself.

King Nebby went to Shadrach's house first.
Shadrach was cunning and wise. Full of knowledge and wisdom was he.
A house made of books was the best thing for him, because he loved to read.
Shadrach was blowing his shofar, when King Nebby found the young lad.
The Wolf King knocked on the door and said: "Is it true, O Shadrach, do not ye
serve my gods, nor worship the golden image which I have set up?" (Daniel 3:14)

"I tell you the truth I do, I do. I will not worship you, or your statue.
If you take away my clothes, or chase me afar.
I won't care, we Hebrew boys know who we are.
I'm not careful to say this. Afraid? No way!
I will not give in, no matter what you say.
So, King Nebby, please just go away!"

This made the Wolf King madder then mad.
He huffed, and he puffed, until his fury rose up like a fire in his bones.
King Nebby opened his mouth and let out a scorching great groan.
Out of his mouth flew hot steamy fire.
The smoke from the scene rose higher and higher.

While the naysayers looked on in dismay,
the young Hebrew boy used wisdom to get away.
Shadrach ran as fast as he could.
Over the hills and through the woods to Meshach's house,
cause King Nebby was up to no good!

Now, Meshach's house was built of faith, covered in bronze and blue. In times of trouble people looked to him. His strength was tried and true. He always practiced patience, cause that's how his faith grew.

Both Hebrew boys sat peacefully,
not knowing the danger nearby.
They discussed the precepts in Torah,
while King Nebby desired for them to die.

The big bad Wolf King knocked on the door and said:
"Is it true, Oh Shadrach, and Meshach, do not ye serve
my gods, nor worship the golden image which I have
set up?" (Daniel 3:14]

Meshach and Shadrach both replied:
"We tell you the truth, we do, we do.
We will not worship you, nor your statue.
If you take away our clothes, our house, or chase us afar.
We won't care, because we Hebrew boys know who we are.
We're not careful to say this. Afraid? No way!
We will not give in, no matter what you say.
So, King Nebby, please just go away!"

The Wolf King grew madder than madder, then madder than mad.
He huffed, and he puffed until his fury rose up like fire in his bones.
King Nebby opened his mouth and let out a scorching great groan.
Out of his mouth flew hot steamy fire.
The smoke from the scene rose higher and higher.

All the naysayers looked on in dismay,
while the two Hebrew boys used Meshach's
good old faithful back door to get away.
Both boys ran as fast as they could.
They ran over the hills and through the woods
to Abednego's house, cause King Nebby was up to no good.

Abednego's house was the strongest of the three,
because Abednego built his house on charity.
Some people look down on charity. They don't believe it always wins.
But did you know charity covers a multitude of sins? (1 PETER 4:8).
Charity is one of the greatest forces against evil we possess.
The perfect building material to keep out a big bad Wolf King,
or any other pest, I must confess.

So, the three little Hebrew boys sat in Abednego's house,
praying towards the east.
When along came a knock at the door from that troublesome beast.

The Wolf King knocked on the door and said:
"Is it true, O Shradrach, Meshach, and Abednego, do not ye serve my gods,
nor worship the golden image which I have set up?"(Daniel 3:14)

Abednego stood up at the door and said:
"Oh King Nebby, my brothers have told you twice before,
Yahuah is faithful to protect us and keep you from coming through this door.
And even if He does not deliver us today.
We just want you to know, we will never bow down to you or your gods,
NO WAY!"

Then, Shadrach, Meshach and Abednego replied:
"We tell you the truth we do, we do.
We will not worship you, or your statue.
If you take away our clothes, our houses, and chase us afar.
We won't care, because we three little Hebrew boys know who we are.
We're not careful to say this. Afraid? No way!
We will not give in no matter what you say.
So, King Nebby, please just go away."

This made the Wolf King madder than he had ever been.
He huffed and he puffed. And he huffed and he puffed again!
Then, King Nebby huffed and he puffed, harder than he had ever huffed
and puffed before, until his fury rose up like a fire in his bones.
King Nebby opened his mouth and let out a scorching great groan.
Out of his mouth flew blazing hot steamy fire.
The smoke from the scene rose higher and higher.
The house burned and burned.
The three little Hebrew boys prayed, they were not concerned.

What do you think the three Hebrew boys were praying about?

If you were in this firey tribulation with them, what would you pray?

_____
_____
_____
_____
_____
_____

All the naysayers looked on and were amazed.
The three little Hebrew boys sat in the house untouched by the firey blaze.
As mad as he was, King Nebby's fire could not stand,
against the house made from charity, the strongest quality known to man.
Shocked at how the house still stood strong and unburned,
King Nebby and the Chaldeans looked in the window taking turns.
Unharmed in the house were the three Hebrews boys.
Unphased by the fire, no char nor smoke.
The three little Hebrew boys made the Wolf King look like a joke.

King Nebby was no longer mad, he was shocked and amazed.
He fell to his knees and cried as he prayed,
"I don't believe what I see, in the beginning there were only three.
Now I see four!
Could it be the son of Yah has been added to the score?"
The Wolf King bowed down, in awe of the ALMIGHTY.
"Please come out Hebrew boys; teach me how to worship Him rightly."

Shadrach, Meshach, and Abednego came out of the house. "And the princes, governors, and captains, and the king's counsellors, being gathered together, saw these men, upon whose bodies the fire had no power, nor was an hair of their head singed, neither were their coats changed, nor the smell of fire had passed on them.

Then Nebuchadnezzar spake, and said, Blessed be the God of Shadrach, Meshach, and Abednego, who hath sent his angel, and delivered his servants that trusted in him, and have changed the king's word, and yielded their bodies, that they might not serve nor worship any god, except their own God. Therefore I make a decree, That every people, nation, and language, which speak anything amiss against the God of Shadrach, Meshach, and Abednego, shall be cut in pieces, and their houses shall be made a dunghill: because there is no other God that can deliver after this sort." (Daniel 3:27-29)

The three little Hebrew boys, Shadrach, Meshach, and Abednego
stood on righteousness and ran away from sin and strife.
Not giving into the temptations of fitting in (Romans 12:2, 1John 2:15)
or saving their life. (Matt 16:25, Matt 10:28)
Just like the Hebrew boys, children of Yisrael should always
righteously stand. (Ephesians 6:11-20)
All other ground is sinking sand.

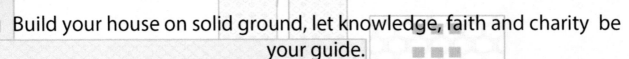

Build your house on solid ground, let knowledge, faith and charity be your guide.
Above all else, remember CHARITY conquers all, even anger and pride.
(Corinthians 13:1- 13)

Charity is more powerful than a burning ember.
And good little Hebrew boys and girls should always remember:
Charity begins with your two little hands,
Christ says: "If ye love me, keep my commands." (John 14:15)
Start with showing charity at home
towards father, mother, daughter and son.

"The first of all the commandments is, Hear, O Israel; The Lord our God is one Lord: And thou shalt love the Lord thy God with all thy heart, and with all thy soul, and with all thy mind, and with all thy strength: this is the first commandment. And the second is like, namely this, Thou shalt love thy neighbour as thyself. There is none other commandment greater than these. And the scribe said unto him, Well, Master, thou hast said the truth: for there is one God; and there is none other but he." (Mark 12:29-32)

About the Author

Keturah Rena spends much of her day trying to maximize her PROVERBS 31, by investing in herself and her entrepreneurial subsidies. Not only is she an author, but she is also a Virtual Assistant, a Crafts Merchant, and Teachers Pay Teachers content producer. Between providing for her house and homeschooling, this mother of four has her hands full. Keturah's passion for education drives her in contributing to the raising up a strong, vibrant, and awakened generation through her businesses and writing. This author/illustrator relies heavily on prayer and direction from Yahuah to help her produce fantastic content for all ages. She refers to it as Yah working through her hands. With no formal training, it is obvious prayer is paying off!

Authors Note

Thank you so much for purchasing my book. I pray it was as much of a blessing to you as it has been for me. My goal for this book was to make a biblical story come to life for our future generations. To help me stay true to my mission, I have created amazing study guides to help both children and parents drive home the key biblical elements. The study guide is free and is accessible at https://iammediabooks.com/3-little-hebrew-boys.

All of the lessons from the study guide I have personally taught via video. If you are interested in the video version of the lessons, they are available via Youtube at https://www.youtube.com/channel/UCGbLE6UahOKBRlpZoimHySQ/videos.

May Yah bless you and your family. I love you to Yah and back, Shalom!

Made in the USA
Middletown, DE
14 April 2021